Big Spider

Sean Taylor

Illustrated by Adrienne Kennaway

RIGBY

Once there was a big spider.
In fact he was a VERY BIG spider.

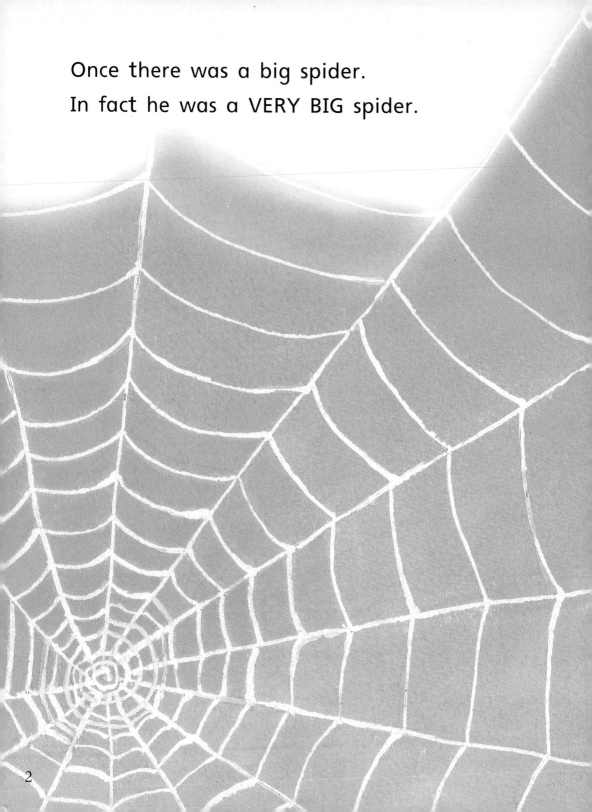

Big Spider's friend Yellow Bird flew by.
"Have you heard?" asked Yellow Bird.
"There is going to be a party in the North!"

A party! Big Spider liked the sound of that.
There would be lots of food!

Then his friend Tree Frog hopped by.
"Good news!" said Tree Frog.
"There is going to be a party in the South!"

Big Spider felt even more excited.
And even more hungry.

Then his friend Bush Pig came by.
"Guess what?" said Bush Pig.
"There is going to be a party in the East!"
Big Spider was beginning to feel confused.

Then Baboon strolled by.

"Come on!" said Baboon.

"There is going to be a party in the West!"

How was Big Spider going to get
to ALL the parties?

He tied four strings round his waist.
He gave each of his friends a string.
He asked them to give the string
a tug when their party started.
That way he would not miss a thing.

Big Spider was pleased. All he had to do was wait for the first tug. But the parties all started at the same time.

So Yellow Bird, Tree Frog, Bush Pig and
Baboon all tugged at the same time!
Big Spider could not move.

His friends thought he must be asleep.
So they tugged harder.
They tugged until Big Spider's belly
got smaller and smaller and smaller.

And that is why spiders have got long
legs and tiny, little bellies.